# Ocean Life

## AMERICAN MUSEUM OF NATURAL HISTORY

### FEATURING DIORAMAS FROM THE
### IRMA AND PAUL MILSTEIN FAMILY HALL OF OCEAN LIFE

About 3.5 billion years ago, the ocean gave rise to the first life on earth. Today, our planet's oceans are home to an amazing diversity of life in a wide range of habitats from tropical coral reefs to the frigid polar seas.

The **Irma and Paul Milstein Family Hall of Ocean Life** highlights the dramatic and complex web of life beneath the waves in an immersive gallery watched over by one of the Museum's most iconic exhibits: a ninety-four-foot-long, twenty-one-thousand-pound model of a blue whale. Habitat dioramas in this grand hall provide portraits of marine species, while exhibits on the mezzanine showcase a variety of ocean habitats, including scenes from the ancient seas.

Many parts of the modern ocean are still poorly known, and less than 5 percent of the deep ocean has been explored. It's hard to comprehend how something as huge and mysterious as the ocean can be fragile, but the threats are real. Some marine species are being driven to the edge of extinction by overfishing, while global climate change, development, and pollution threaten delicate ocean ecosystems. Understanding the ocean and its inhabitants is key to safeguarding the future.

The American Museum of Natural History in New York City is one of the world's preeminent scientific, educational, and cultural institutions, drawing millions of visitors each year. Visit amnh.org for more information.

*Pomegranate*

All of the dioramas depicted in these line drawings are found in the **Irma and Paul Milstein Family Hall of Ocean Life** at the American Museum of Natural History in New York City.

1. **Coral Reef** (detail left)
   *Off the Coast of Andros Island, The Bahamas*

2. **Tiger Shark** (*Galeocerdo cuvier*)
   *Found Near Warm-water Shores Throughout the World*

3. **Walrus** (*Odobenus rosmarus*)
   *Ice Floe in the Bering Sea*

4. **Dolphin** (*Delphinus delphis*) **and Yellowfin Tuna** (*Thunnus albacares*)
   *Found off the Eastern Coast of the Tropical Pacific Ocean, Near Mexico and Central America*

5. **Dolphin** (*Delphinus delphis*) **and Yellowfin Tuna** (*Thunnus albacares*)
   *Found off the Eastern Coast of the Tropical Pacific Ocean, Near Mexico and Central America*

6. **Coral Reef** (detail right)
   *Off the Coast of Andros Island, The Bahamas*

7. **Life in the Ordovician Seas**
   *Late Ordovician Period (450 Million Years Ago), Present-day Ohio*

8. **Life in the Ordovician Seas**
   *Late Ordovician Period (450 Million Years Ago), Present-day Ohio*

9. **Life in the Permian Seas** (detail left)
   *Permian Period (270 Million Years Ago), Present-day Texas*

10. **Life in the Permian Seas** (detail right)
    *Permian Period (270 Million Years Ago), Present-day Texas*

11. **Northern Sea Lion** (*Eumetopias jubatus*)
    *Aleutian Islands and the Pribilof Islands, North Pacific Ocean*

12. **Life in the Cretaceous Seas**
    *Late Cretaceous Period (70 Million Years Ago), Present-day Tennessee*

13. **Coral Reefs, Powderblue Surgeonfish** (*Acanthurus leucosternon*)
    *Indo-Pacific Coral Reef*

14. **Harbor Seal** (*Phoca vitulina*)
    *Kitovi Rookery, St. Paul Island, Alaska*

15. **Sperm Whale** (*Physeter macrocephalus*) **and Giant Squid** (*Architeuthis dux*)
    *Found in Ice-free Waters Around the World*

16. **Sargasso Sea**
    *Atlantic Ocean*

17. **West Indian Manatee** (*Trichechus manatus*)
    *Found in Tropical and Subtropical Regions of the Atlantic Ocean and Caribbean Sea*

18. **Northern Elephant Seal** (*Mirounga angustirostris*)
    *Guadalupe Island, Lower California, Mexico*

19. **Blue Whale** (*Balaenoptera musculus*)
    *Sighted in All of the Earth's Oceans*

20. **Sea Otter** (*Enhydra lutris*)
    *Found in the Shallow Coastal Waters of the North Pacific*

Pomegranate Communications, Inc.
19018 NE Portal Way, Portland OR 97230
800 227 1428   www.pomegranate.com

*Pomegranate's mission is to invigorate, illuminate, and inspire through art.*

© 2017 American Museum of Natural History, New York
Photographs © AMNH. Photography by Craig Chesek, Denis Finnin, Roderick Mickens, and Matt Shanley, AMNH.

Item No. CB186

Designed by Patrice Morris

Printed in Korea

26 25 24 23 22 21 20 19 18 17    10 9 8 7 6 5 4 3 2 1

Distributed by Pomegranate Europe Ltd.
'number three', Siskin Drive, Middlemarch Business Park
Coventry CV3 4FJ, UK
+44 (0)24 7621 4461   sales@pomegranate.com

1. Coral Reef

2. **Tiger Shark** (*Galeocerdo cuvier*)

3. **Walrus** (*Odobenus rosmarus*)

4. **Dolphin** (*Delphinus delphis*) **and Yellowfin Tuna** (*Thunnus albacares*)

5. **Dolphin** (*Delphinus delphis*) **and Yellowfin Tuna** (*Thunnus albacares*)

6. Coral Reef

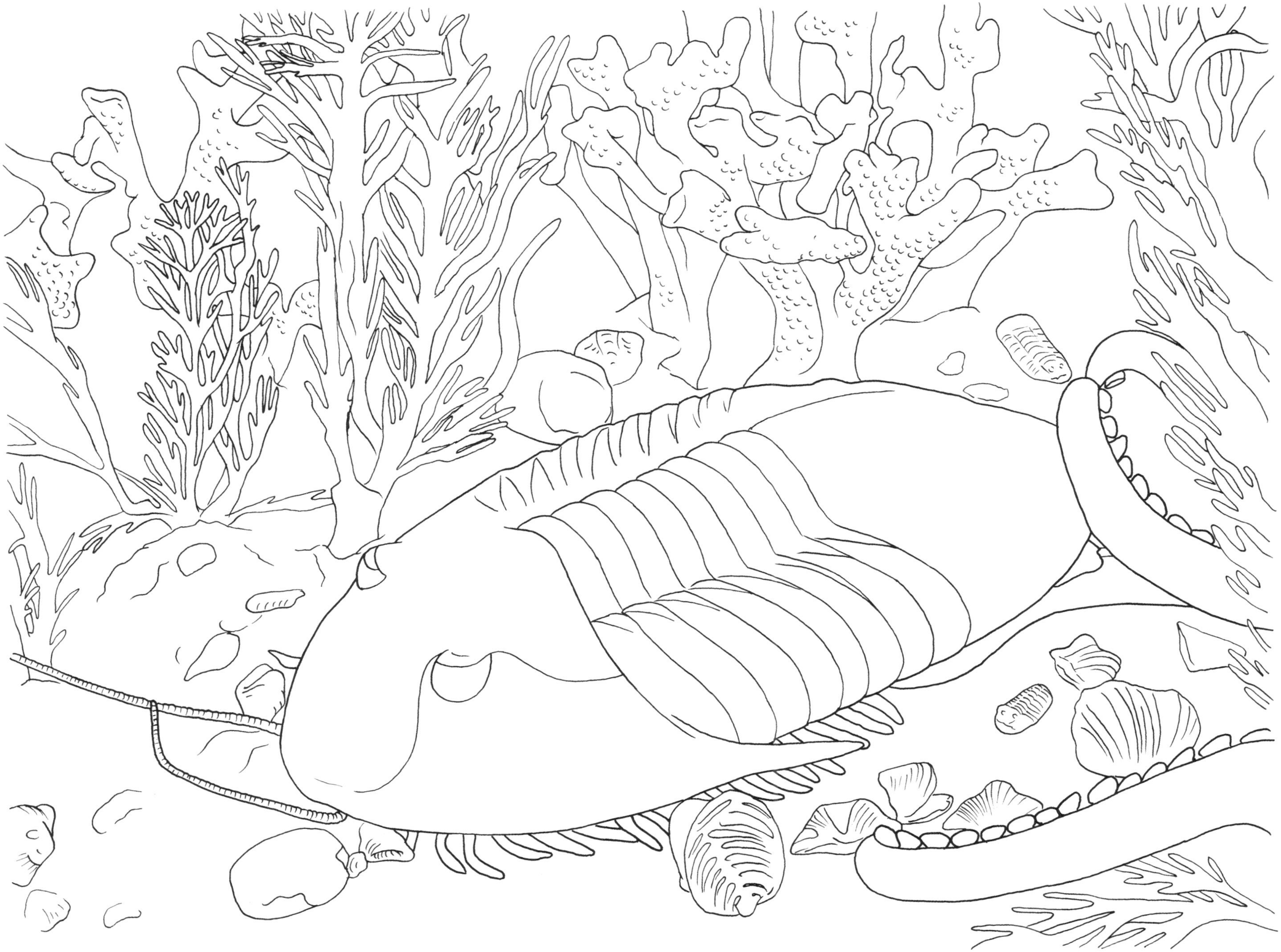

8. **Life in the Ordovician Seas**

**9. Life in the Permian Seas**

10. **Life in the Permian Seas**

11. **Northern Sea Lion** (*Eumetopias jubatus*)

13. Coral Reefs, Powderblue Surgeonfish (*Acanthurus leucosternon*)

14. **Harbor Seal** (*Phoca vitulina*)

15. **Sperm Whale** (*Physeter macrocephalus*) **and Giant Squid** (*Architeuthis dux*)

16. Sargasso Sea

17. West Indian Manatee (*Trichechus manatus*)

18. **Northern Elephant Seal** (*Mirounga angustirostris*)

19. **Blue Whale** (*Balaenoptera musculus*)

20. **Sea Otter** (*Enhydra lutris*)

Draw and color your own picture here!

*Draw and color your own picture here!*

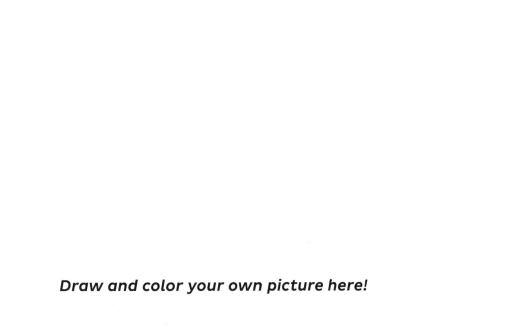

**Draw and color your own picture here!**